KU-012-560

This
STICK MAN
annual belongs to

Niraashini: ~~_____~~ _____

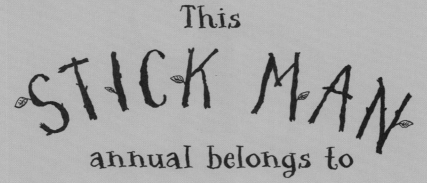

ALISON
GREEN
BOOKS

First published in the UK in 2018 by Alison Green Books
An imprint of Scholastic Children's Books
Euston House, 24 Eversholt Street
London NW1 1DB, UK
A division of Scholastic Ltd
www.scholastic.co.uk
London – New York – Toronto – Sydney – Auckland
Mexico City – New Delhi – Hong Kong
Based on Stick Man, the original picture book
by Julia Donaldson and Axel Scheffler

Text copyright © Julia Donaldson 2008, 2012 and 2018
Illustrations copyright © Axel Scheffler 2008, 2012 and 2018

ISBN: 978 1407 17454 9
All rights reserved
Printed in Malaysia

1 3 5 7 9 8 6 4 2

The moral rights of Julia Donaldson and Axel Scheffler have been asserted.
Papers used by Scholastic Children's Books are made from wood
grown in sustainable forests.

Contents

The Family Tree

This is Stick Man's home, he lives here with his family.

My Home

Draw a picture of your house and everyone who lives in it.

Run, Stick Man!

Colour in Stick Man and the
dog as they run through the park.

Hidden Holiday Words

These words are all to do with summer holidays.
Can you find them in the word search?

SEAGULL

SEAGULL

SHELL

BUCKET

S	F	S	H	E	L	L	D	I	S
R	P	X	N	E	A	N	B	Q	E
M	Z	D	G	T	W	I	O	J	A
C	O	V	D	I	H	G	A	F	G
M	B	I	W	A	Y	U	T	L	U
P	A	F	R	P	Q	T	O	A	L
C	R	A	B	E	R	L	N	G	L
A	R	O	G	N	P	F	R	O	N
S	A	N	D	C	A	S	T	L	E
B	U	C	K	E	T	T	I	C	B

SANDCASTLE

CRAB

BOAT

9

Nesting

Stick Man meets two swans on his journey. They have three eggs that hatch into baby swans. Decorate the eggs below with lots of patterns and colours.

TOP TIP

You could draw stripes, zigzags, dots or even stars.

Colour Me In

Jolly Jokes

Make your friends laugh with these silly Stick Man jokes.

Q: What's brown and sticky?
A: A stick!

Q: What did the little tree say to the big tree?
A: Leaf me alone!

Q: What do you call a man with a spade on his head?
A: Doug.

Q: Why did the crab go to prison?
A: He couldn't stop pinching things.

Q: Why did the shell blush?
A: Because the sea-weed.

Q: What did the beach say to the wave?
A: "Long tide, no sea."

Knock, knock.
Who's there?
Who.
Who who?
Are you an owl?

Q: Why did the leaf go to the doctor?
A: It was feeling green!

Q: Why do bananas wear sunscreen at the beach?
A: So they don't peel.

A-Z with Stick Man

A is for Autumn

Autumn is the months of September, October and November. After summer, it starts to get darker much earlier in the day, and it feels colder too. The leaves on the trees turn red and orange and begin to fall. Animals such as squirrels and bears start storing food in preparation for winter, because that's when they hibernate. Also, birds begin to fly away to warmer places – this is called migration.

B is for Butterfly

Butterflies start their lives as little eggs, and later hatch into caterpillars. When they lay their eggs, butterfly mums usually choose a leaf that their baby will like to eat, so that the caterpillar has something yummy close-by when it hatches. When caterpillars are fully grown they build themselves a special house called a chrysalis or a cocoon. They rest inside it for a while – sometimes this is days and sometimes it's months – and when they're ready to come out of the chrysalis, they are no longer a caterpillar but a butterfly!

C is for Cygnet

Baby swans are called cygnets. Swans sit on their eggs for six weeks until they hatch. After hatching, cygnets stay with their parents for six weeks, until they are old enough to look after themselves. Cygnets then leave and find a new swan family to stay with for four years, until they are grown up.

D is for Duckling

Baby ducks are called ducklings. When they hatch, their mum takes them to the nearest water to teach them to swim. They need to stay close to her so that she can make their fluffy feathers waterproof and help them find the right things to eat.

E is for Earthworm

Earthworms can be anything from one millimetre to three metres long! To help the soil they live in stay healthy, they mix it by wriggling through it. That's why they are usually found far underground.

F is for Forest

You can find all sorts of animals in forests. Next time you go for a walk , see how many different types of animals you can spot. Forests are made up of all different kinds of trees, and in autumn the floor is covered with crunchy leaves.

G is for Grass

There are over eleven thousand types of grasses. Even bamboo is actually a grass. The one you probably see the most is the grass in gardens and forests. Grass is the main food for many animals, so where you find grass you are likely to spot some creatures too.

Speedy Sticks and Pesky Pups

Roll the dice and see if you can help Stick Man go home! If you land on a dog, follow it down, and if you land on Stick Man, follow him up.

1. Put your counters on START. To find out who will go first, each player needs to roll the dice. The player with the highest score can start the game.

You will need:
- A dice
- Some small objects to use as counters

2. Take turns to roll the dice and move forward or backward the correct number of spaces. Don't forget:
- Landing on a Stick Man means you can move forward extra spaces.
- Landing on a dog means you must move back.

3. The first player to land on FINISH wins the game!

FINISH

28

27
Oh no!
Back to
number 21

26

25

20

22

Energy
boost! Up to
number 25

24

21

19
Dogs on
leads! Up to
number 21

18

Fetch! Back
to number 16

16

15

17

10

11
A near
miss! Up to
number 15

12

13
Run!
Back to
number 5

14

9

8

7
Caught!
Back to
number 1

6

5

START

1

2

3
A shortcut!
Up to
number 6

4

Counting Games

Count the pictures and write the number in each box.

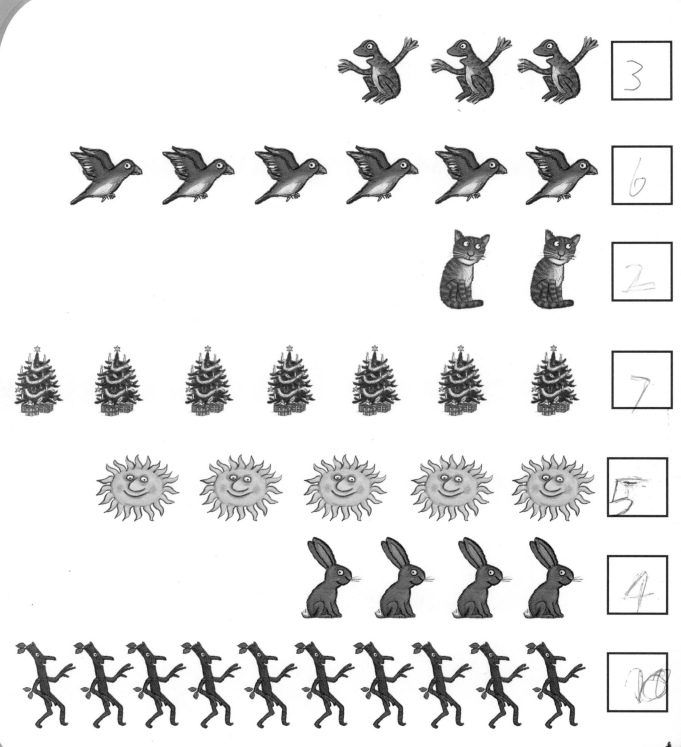

3

6

2

7

5

4

10

Shadow Pairs

Match the shadows to their owners.

crab

snowman

Mystery Swimmer

Who is splish-splashing in the river? Join the dots to find out.

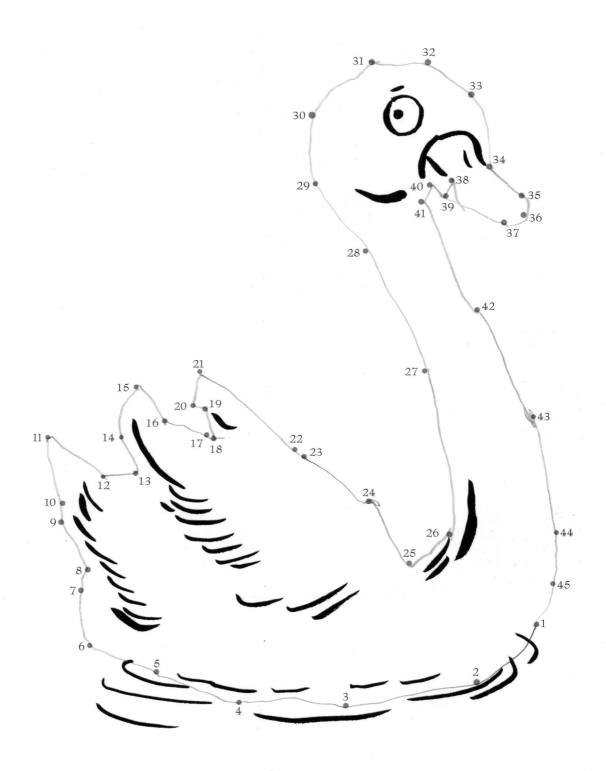

Design Your Sandcastle

Add decorations and create your own flag to
make a wonderful sandcastle.

A-Z with Stick Man

H is for Hibernate

In winter, many animals curl up and sleep through the coldest months. They spend autumn collecting food in a warm, dark, cosy spot that they will be safe to sleep in. Then they eat all their food so they don't wake up hungry.

I is for Insects

Insects can be found everywhere, and they love plants and trees. Bumblebees are in danger of going extinct. If you see one, be sure to leave it alone and not hurt it. We need bumblebees, as they help plants survive.

J is for Jackdaw

A jackdaw is a small black crow. They can be found in fields, woods, parks and gardens. They eat insects, grass and plants.

K is for Kitten

Baby cats are called kittens. They sleep up to eighteen hours a day, and when they are born they can't see. When they grow up, their sense of smell is fourteen times stronger than a human's.

L is for Lamb

Baby sheep are called lambs. Lambs are usually born on their own or with a twin, but sometimes three or four babies are born together. When lambs are first born, they only drink milk. From week one onwards, they can eat grass and hay, and drink water too.

M is for Magpie

Magpies are black-and-white birds. They love collecting shiny things to put in their nests. They are one of the most intelligent birds, and one of the only animals that can recognise itself in the mirror.

N is for Nest

Birds make their nests out of twigs and grass, and can stay in them for up to six months. Often, they will lay their eggs in a nest, and then when the babies are born they add their babies' eggshells to the nest. If you ever find a bird's nest, don't touch it or the bird won't be able to live there any more.

Which is Which?

Fill in the missing letters, and then draw lines to match the animals to their names.

RABBIT

CRAB

SWAN

CAT

SHEEP

SQUIRREL

24

Back to the Nest

Follow the maze and lead the baby swan back to its family.

Oh I Do Like to be Beside the Seaside

Draw some boats on the water and a beautiful sky.

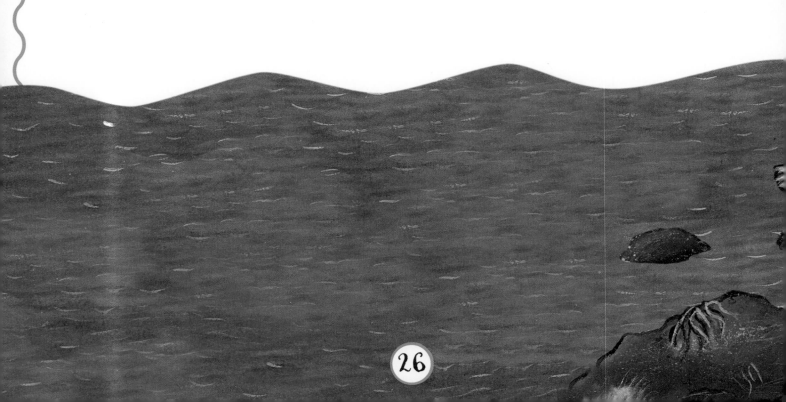

Sing Along with Stick Man

Row, Row, Row Your Boat

Row, row, row your boat
Gently down the stream
Merrily, merrily, merrily, merrily
Life is but a dream.

Row, row, row your boat
Gently up the creek
If you see a little mouse
Don't forget to squeak!

Row, row, row your boat
Gently down the stream
If you see a crocodile
Don't forget to scream!

If You're Happy and You Know It

If you're happy and you know it, clap your hands. (Clap, clap.)
If you're happy and you know it, clap your hands. (Clap, clap.)
If you're happy and you know it, and you really want to show it,
If you're happy and you know it, clap your hands. (Clap, clap.)

If you're angry and you know it, stamp your feet. (Stamp, stamp.)
If you're angry and you know it, stamp your feet. (Stamp, stamp.)

If you're angry and you know it, and you really want to show it,
If you're angry and you know it, stamp your feet. (Stamp, stamp.)

If you're happy and you know it, shout "Hooray!" ("Hooray!")
If you're happy and you know it, shout "Hooray!" ("Hooray!")
If you're happy and you know it, and you really want to show it,
If you're happy and you know it, shout "Hooray!" ("Hooray!")

Colour Me In

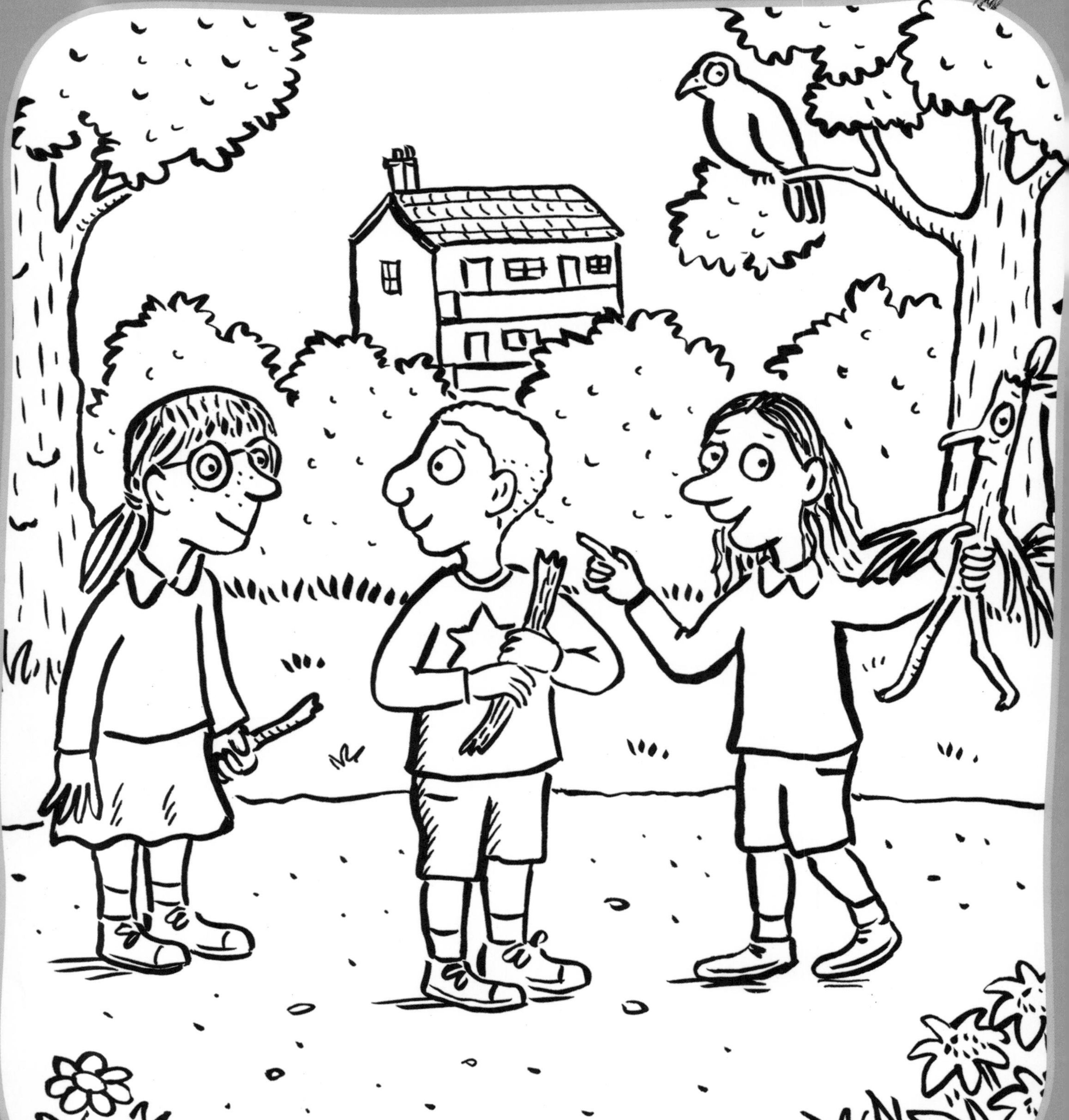

Beach I Spy

What can you see at the beach? List everything in the picture below and then play I Spy with a friend!

Let It Snow

Draw some friends for Stick Man to play with in the snow.

O is for Oak

The oak tree is a large deciduous tree, which means its leaves change with the seasons. Oak trees grow acorns, but not until the tree is at least forty years old. Acorns can be found on the floor around the tree in autumn, and are often collected by squirrels to eat.

P is for Pine

Pine trees are evergreen trees, which means their leaves stay green all year round. They can age as old as 1,000 years. Their leaves are called needles, and have a very unique smell. Pine trees also produce pinecones, which are often used at Christmas as decorations.

Q is for Quills

The sharp pointy bits on hedgehogs are called quills. They use them when they are frightened, to scare off other animals. They also roll into a tight ball to try and hide. Hedgehogs are nocturnal, which means they sleep in the day and come out at night. They are very good at seeing in the dark.

R is for Rabbit

Baby rabbits are called kittens. Rabbits have strong back legs for kicking and running, and long ears. They eat plants and grass, and live in underground tunnels called burrows.

S is for Spring

Spring takes place in the months of March, April and May. This is when animals that went into hibernation in the winter wake up. Plants begin to grow again, and blossoms can be seen on trees. Lots of baby animals are born in the spring.

T is for Tadpole

Frog mums lay thousands of eggs at a time, and their eggs hatch into . . . tadpoles! Tadpoles live in water and can swim very fast. After a few weeks they start to grow arms and legs and their mouths get wider, until they grow up into frogs.

The Stick Man Quiz

Who chases Stick Man through the park?

A: Cat ☐
B: Dog ☑
C: Tiger ☐
D: Bird ☐

How many children does Stick Man have?

A: One ☐
B: Seven ☐
C: Three ☑
D: Ten ☐

What colour is Stick Man?

A: Yellow ☐
B: Brown ☑
C: Pink ☐
D: Blue ☐

Who does Stick Man find in the chimney?

A: Easter Bunny ☐
B: Santa Claus ☑
C: Rudolph ☐
D: His wife ☐

What do the swans think Stick Man is?

A: A carrot ☑
B: A duck ☐
C: Food ☐
D: A twig ☐

True or False?

Decide which of these is true or false.

Stick Man lives in a bush with his stick family.

True ☐   False ☑

Stick Man gets used as a pooh-stick and thrown into the river.

True ☑   False ☐

Stick Man joins the people to sing Christmas carols with them.

True ☐   False ☑

Stick Man helps Santa to deliver presents to the sleeping children.

True ☑   False ☐

Stick Man's children are in bed when they hear a noise.

True ☑   False ☐

Your Own Snowman

Finish drawing the snowman. Add some decorations – don't forget his nose, eyes and buttons!

Say What You See

Can you find and circle all of the things in this picture?

Dog   Frog   House   Swan   Stick Man

Odd One Out

Find and circle the odd one out in these sequences.

41

Help the Dog Home

Follow the line to lead the dog to his owner.

Spot the Difference

Find the four differences between these two pictures.

Stick Man's Journey

Follow Stick Man down the path, completing tasks along the w

1. Stick Man is married to
Stick Lady. Draw them
together here.

2. On his journey, Stick Man
picked up by a dog. What nois
do dogs make? Match all of th
animals with their noises.

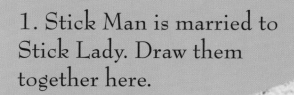

Dog   Meow
Duck   Quack
Cat   Tweet
Bird   Woof

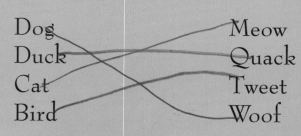

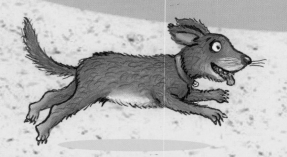

3. When Stick Man is thrown
into the water, does he sink or
float? Write your answer here: _____

6. At the seaside, Stick Man sees a sandcastle. Draw your own sandcastle here:

7. On his journey, Stick Man meets a swan. Can you find one hiding on this page?

5. Stick Man gets lost in the cold. How would you describe snow? Pick words from the list.

Warm	Icy	Smelly
White	Fluffy	Cold
	Pink	Sparkly

4. Colour in this picture.

Transform Your Tree

Draw your own decorations for a beautiful Christmas tree –
and don't forget to finish it with a shining star on top!

Mystery Visitor

Follow the dots to see who this is.

A-Z with Stick Man

U is for Upstream

Rivers and streams often have currents. A current is when the water moves strongly in one direction. The direction it is moving in is called upstream, and the opposite direction is called downstream. The current can change depending on the weather and time of day.

V is for Violets

Violets are purple flowers often found in forests and gardens. They are perennial, which means they flower in spring and summer, die in winter, and then come back the next spring. This can continue for over ten years in the right conditions.

W is for Willow

Willow trees are some of the best trees to grow in cold, rainy countries. They love damp environments. Because the trees often grow beside rivers, any twigs that break off are carried downstream where they can then take root further away so more willow trees can grow.

X is for Xylem

Xylem is the part of the plant that takes water from the roots to the leaves. It also makes the stem of the plants stronger.

Y is for Yew

Yew trees can grow up to twenty metres tall. The bark is reddish-brown, and looks like it is peeling. Yew trees are some of the oldest trees. Yew hedges are perfect for birds to nest in, and can be found in forests and woods.

Z is for Zero

Water freezes into ice at zero degrees. This means that for it to snow it has to be very cold, so the rain turns into ice. To make a snowman you need a lot of snow, but make sure you wear gloves!

Christmas Conundrum

Find the festive words in the word search below.

TREE

STAR

SNOWMAN

Z	S	N	O	W	M	A	N	I	P
R	T	Q	N	E	A	N	B	Q	R
M	A	K	G	T	R	E	E	J	E
C	R	O	S	I	H	G	A	F	S
M	B	G	W	N	Y	U	T	L	E
P	A	F	R	P	O	T	O	A	N
S	A	N	T	A	R	W	N	G	T
A	R	O	G	N	P	F	M	O	N
Q	P	H	Y	U	Y	O	F	A	X
R	O	B	I	N	T	T	T	I	C	N

ROBIN

PRESENT

SANTA

Sweet Dreams

Stick Man is sleeping – can you draw what he is dreaming about?

Christmas Sing-Along

Get in the holiday mood and sing these songs
with your friends or family.

Jingle Bells

Dashing through the snow,
In a one horse open sleigh.
Over the fields we go,
Laughing all the way.
Bells on bob tail ring,
making spirits bright.
What fun it is to laugh and sing,
A sleighing song tonight.

Oh, jingle bells, jingle bells,
Jingle all the way.
Oh, what fun it is to ride,
In a one horse open sleigh.
Jingle bells, jingle bells,
Jingle all the way.
Oh, what fun it is to ride
In a one horse open sleigh.

O Christmas Tree!

~~O Christmas Tree! O Christmas Tree!~~
~~Thy leaves are so unchanging;~~
~~O Christmas Tree! O Christmas Tree!~~
~~Thy leaves are so unchanging;~~
Not only green when summer's here,
But also when 'tis cold and drear.
O Christmas Tree! O Christmas Tree!
Thy leaves are so unchanging!

O Christmas Tree! O Christmas Tree!
Much pleasure thou can'st give me;
O Christmas Tree! O Christmas Tree!
Much pleasure thou can'st give me;
How often has the Christmas tree
Afforded me the greatest glee!
O Christmas Tree! O Christmas Tree!
Much pleasure thou can'st give me.

Find Stick Man's Home

Guide Stick Man through the maze,
all the way home to his family.

Stick Family Presents

Santa has brought lots of lovely presents for Stick Man
and his family. Draw a present you would like.

Christmas Day Feast

Draw what you would like to eat on Christmas Day,
even if it's ice cream for breakfast . . .

Stick Family Christmas

Draw Stick Man and his family enjoying Christmas Day.

Answers

Hidden Holiday Words

S	F	S	H	E	L	L	D	I	S
R	P	X	N	E	A	N	B	Q	E
M	Z	D	G	T	W	I	O	J	A
C	O	V	D	I	H	G	A	F	G
M	B	I	W	A	Y	U	T	L	U
P	A	F	R	P	Q	T	O	A	L
C	R	A	B	E	R	L	N	G	L
A	R	O	G	N	P	F	R	O	N
S	A	N	D	C	A	S	T	L	E
B	U	C	K	E	T	T	I	C	B

Counting Games

3 Frogs
6 Birds
2 Cats
7 Christmas Trees
5 Suns
4 Rabbits
10 Stick Men

Shadow Pairs

Mystery Swimmer

Which is Which?

RABBIT
CRAB
SWAN
CAT
SHEEP
SQUIRREL

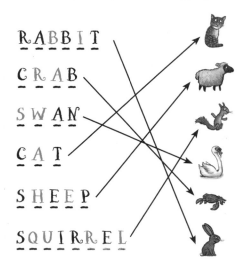

Swan Family Reunion

Stick Man Quiz

1. B   4. B
2. C   5. D
3. B

True or False?

1. False
2. True
3. False
4. True
5. True

Odd One Out

Help The Dog Home

Spot the Difference

Stick Man's Journey

2. Dog — Meow
Duck — Quack
Cat — Tweet
Bird — Woof

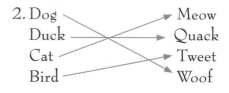

3. Float

5. White, cold, icy, sparkly, fluffy

7. Behind the trees

Mystery Visitor

Christmas Conundrum

Z	S	N	O	W	M	A	N	I	P
R	T	Q	N	E	A	N	B	Q	R
M	A	K	G	T	R	E	E	J	E
C	R	O	S	I	H	G	A	F	S
M	B	G	W	N	Y	U	T	L	E
P	A	F	R	P	O	T	O	A	N
S	A	N	T	A	R	W	N	G	T
A	R	O	G	N	P	F	M	O	N
Q	P	H	Y	U	Y	O	F	A	X
R	O	B	I	N	T	T	I	C	N

Find Stick Man's Home